Mystery Mob
and the
Magic Bottle

Roger Hurn

Illustrated by
Stik

RISING STARS

Rising Stars UK Ltd.
7 Hatchers Mews, Bermondsey Street, London SE1 3GS
www.risingstars-uk.com

The right of Roger Hurn to be identified as the author of this work has been
asserted by him in accordance with the Copyright, Design and Patents Act
1988.

Published 2007
Reprinted 2009, 2012, 2013, 2015

Text, design and layout © Rising Stars UK Ltd.

Cover design: Button plc
Illustrator: Stik, Bill Greenhead for Illustration
Text design and typesetting: Andy Wilson
Publisher: Gill Budgell
Publishing manager: Sasha Morton
Editor: Catherine Baker
Series consultant: Cliff Moon

British Library Cataloguing in Publication Data.
A CIP record for this book is available from the British Library

ISBN: 978-1-84680-229-4

Printed by Ashford Colour Press Ltd

MIX
Paper from
responsible sources
FSC® C011748
FSC
www.fsc.org

Contents

Meet the Mystery Mob

Name:

Gummy

FYI: Gummy hasn't got much brain – and even fewer teeth.

Loves: Soup.

Hates: Toffee chews.

Fact: The brightest thing about him is his shirt.

Name:

Lee

FYI: If Lee was any cooler he'd be a cucumber.

Loves: Hip-hop.

Hates: Hopscotch.

Fact: He has his own designer label (which he peeled off a tin).

Name:

FYI: Rob lives in his own world – he's just visiting planet Earth.

Loves: Daydreaming.

Hates: Nightmares.

Fact: Rob always does his homework – he just forgets to write it down.

Name:

Dwayne

FYI: Dwayne is smarter than a tree full of owls.

Loves: Anything complicated.

Hates: Join-the-dots books.

Fact: If he was any brighter you could use him as a floodlight at football matches.

Name:

Chet

FYI: Chet is as brave as a lion with steel jaws.

Loves: Having adventures.

Hates: Knitting.

Fact: He's as tough as the chicken his granny cooks for his tea.

Name:

Adi

FYI: Adi is as happy as a football fan with tickets to the big match.

Loves: Telling jokes.

Hates: Moaning minnies.

Fact: He knows more jokes than a jumbo joke book.

1

A Day at the Beach

The Mystery Mob are spending a day
at the seaside. They've got everything
they need to have a great time.
Rob's got his swimming trunks on.
Lee has his football, Chet has
his stunt kite, Adi has his fishing net
and Gummy has a stick of rock.
Dwayne has a book on beachcombing.

Lee	Why don't we have a game of beach football?
Rob	No. I want to go for a swim. Who's coming with me?
Chet	Not me. The water looks totally freezing. I'm going to fly my kite.
Gummy	That sounds too much like hard work. I think I'll go and buy an ice cream.

Adi   Hey, do you know what kind
of fish goes well with ice cream?

Mystery Mob

No.

Adi   Jellyfish!

Dwayne   Right! That's it.
I'm off beachcombing.
I've got to get away from Adi
and his awful jokes.

Gummy Hold up, Dwayne.
I'm coming with you.

Dwayne Don't you want to go
and get an ice cream?

Gummy No way! Adi's put me right off.
I can't eat ice cream
with a jellyfish. I wanted one
with a chocolate flake.

② Rock Pools

Dwayne and Gummy leave the others and walk off along the beach.

Dwayne Come on, Gummy,
we're beachcombers.
Let's see what we can find.

Gummy What are we looking for?

Dwayne All sorts of stuff.
Hey, there are some rock pools
over there. I bet they'll be full
of crabs and fish and shrimps.

Gummy   How do you know that?

Dwayne   Because of all those big gulls
with sharp beaks sitting
on the rocks. Those guys
just love eating fresh seafood.

Gummy   Wait a minute.
I don't want to go paddling
in the rock pools.

Dwayne   Why not?

Gummy   Well, you say they're full of fish
and crabs and stuff.
So, maybe there's a crocodile
in there as well!

Dwayne Don't worry. There's no chance
of you finding a croc
in these rock pools.

Gummy How can you be so sure?

Dwayne Because the sharks ate them all.

Gummy SHARKS!

Dwayne Relax. I'm only winding you up.
The worst thing that can happen
is if a crab nips you with its claws.

Gummy Well, if you say so.
Er … but what do we do
if we catch a crab?

Dwayne You hold it gently.
I'll look it up in my book
to see what kind of crab it is.
Then we'll put it back
carefully into the pool.

Gummy Right. Hey, I can see a crab.
It's trying to hide under this
seaweed. Hang on. I'll catch it.

Dwayne Take care not to hurt it.
And don't let the greedy gulls
get it. Crabs are their favourite.

Gummy scoops up the tiny crab.

Gummy Gotcha!

Dwayne What does it look like?

Gummy Well, this crab's got sandy claws.

Dwayne You're kidding me. What's
Father Christmas doing here?
He lives at the North Pole –
not in a rock pool.

Gummy What are you on about?
I said sandy claws, not …
oh, I get it. It's another wind-up.

Dwayne That's right. You caught a crab
and *I* caught *you*.

Gummy Huh. Well, I'm fed up with you
tricking me. And I'm fed up
with beachcombing. I'm going
to have a paddle in the sea.

Dwayne Oh come on, Gummy,
don't be like that.

But Gummy jumps out of the rook pool
and runs off down to the sea.
Dwayne races after him.

③

A Green Bottle

Gummy stands in the sea with
his jeans rolled up to his knees.
The waves splash up his legs.
The water's cold. Gummy thinks that
paddling isn't such a great idea
after all. Then he sees a green
glass bottle floating in the water.
Gummy grabs it.

Gummy   Hey, Dwayne. Look at this.

Dwayne   Wow! It's just the sort of bottle a castaway on a desert island would have. Maybe it's got a message inside it.

Gummy   I don't think so. All I can see in there is some smoke.

Dwayne   Smoke? That's a bit weird.

Gummy   And that's not all. I can see two red eyes looking at me.

Dwayne I think you've had too much sun.
Your mum told you to wear
your hat!

Gummy And I'm telling you the truth.
I'm going to pull out this cork
and then you can see
for yourself.

Dwayne (shouting) No, don't do that!

But it's too late. Gummy gives the cork
a tug. The smoke pours out of the bottle.
It swirls like a big, dark storm cloud.
Then it takes the shape of a genie.
The boys can't believe their eyes!

Dwayne Tell me this isn't happening.
Genies aren't for real – are they?

Gummy Well, I'm no expert,
but this one looks like
the real deal to me. Hey!
Maybe he'll grant us three wishes.

Dwayne Well, my first wish is that
you hadn't let him out
of the bottle.

Gummy Doh! Don't waste wishes.
I want to ask him for some
really cool stuff.

Dwayne Like what?

Gummy Like four new front teeth.

Dwayne   Hmmm …
I've got a funny feeling
that this genie is not
a wish-granting kind of guy.

Dwayne is right. The genie is not
a friendly genie.

Genie   Free at last! For 500 years
I have been trapped
in that tiny bottle,
but now I have escaped.
Watch out world, I'm back!
I want revenge …
and I'm going to start with *you*!

Dwayne Hang on – we're the ones
who let you out of the bottle!
Why are you cross with us?

Genie Because it's your unlucky day.
And it just got worse. I'm going
to turn you into little green frogs!

Gummy Yikes – he really is *hopping* mad!

Dwayne Yeah. And if we don't think
of something quickly –
we'll be hopping like mad.

A Nasty Spell

The genie can't resist boasting.

Genie   Don't bother trying to beg
for mercy, you miserable brats!
I am the cruellest and most
powerful genie in all the world!

Gummy   Awesome! Hey, what kind
of magic stuff can you do?

Genie   I can do anything! Turning boys
into frogs is just the start.

Gummy (whispering) This genie is just
a bully who's too big
for his boots.

Dwayne (whispering) Wait a sec.
That gives me an idea.
Do you remember the story
of Puss-in-Boots?

Gummy Yes, but how is that
going to help us?

Dwayne Well, think how Puss
tricked the giant.
Let's see if we can do the same.

Gummy (whispering) But this is a genie, not a giant.

Dwayne (whispering) I know that, but do you have a better idea?

Gummy Er ... no.

Dwayne So let's do it.

The genie is just about to cast his spell
on the boys when Gummy speaks up.

Gummy   Mr Genie, we don't think
you can do lots of magic.
We think you can only do
one simple trick.

Dwayne That's right. Turning Gummy
into a frog is dead easy.
He's already got a big mouth
and no teeth. And he goes green
when he's had too many
cream cakes.

Gummy So, if you want to show off,
why not do a really hard trick?
Like turn yourself into a lion?

The genie sneers at Gummy.
He says he'll turn into a lion
to show just how clever he is.
Then he'll turn the boys into frogs.
But Dwayne shakes his head.

Dwayne No, don't turn into a lion.
That's a piece of cake
for a big tough genie like you.
I mean, any genie can do *big*,
but it takes a totally amazing
genie to do *small*.

This makes the genie very cross indeed.
He roars at the boys. He has really lost
his temper now.

Genie How dare you? I can do *small* better than any genie alive! Shalamazam!

There is a crash of thunder and a puff of smoke. The genie vanishes and a small crab appears in his place.

⑤

Snack Attack

This is just what the boys
have been waiting for. They call
to the gulls by the rock pools.

Dwayne Come and get it, you greedy
gulls. It's lunchtime!

Gummy Grub's up, guys.

A large gull swoops down and snaps up
the crab. In two crunches of its beak
the crab is gone. The boys
give each other high fives.

Dwayne That was a close call.

Gummy Too right. But have we seen
the last of the genie?

Dwayne I don't know for sure.
But I reckon that now
we've given him the bird
he'll leave us alone.

Gummy That's all right then.
Hey, I didn't know
beachcombing was so exciting.
Shall we do some more?

Dwayne No. I've had enough excitement for one day. Why don't we go back and see what the others are doing?

Gummy You're on. Anyway, I can't wait to tell them how we tricked the genie in the bottle. I don't know about frogs, but they're going to go green with envy when they hear about it.

Dwayne True. But there's one thing you *can* say about that genie.

Gummy What's that?

Dwayne He was just sooooo crabby!

About the author

Roger Hurn has:

- been an actor in 'The Exploding Trouser Company'
- played bass guitar in a rock band
- been given the title Malam Oga (wise teacher, big boss!) while on a storytelling trip to Africa.

Now he's a writer, and he hopes you like reading about the Mystery Mob as much as he likes writing about them.

Seashore quiz

Questions

1 What do you get if you cross an elephant with a fish?

2 What washes up on really small beaches?

3 What do you call a fish with no eyes?

4 Why is the ocean wet?

5 What did the sea say to the man?

6 What do sharks eat for dinner?

7 What do you call a witch who lives on the beach?

8 What day do fish really hate?

How did you score?

✋ If you got all eight seashore answers correct, then you are really on the crest of a wave!

✋ If you got six seashore answers correct, then no one's going to kick sand in your face.

✋ If you got fewer than four seashore answers correct, then there's definitely something fishy going on.

When I was a kid

Question   Did you like going to the seaside when you were a kid?

Roger   It was okay, but I didn't like having picnics on the beach.

Question   Why not?

Roger   Because I don't like sand in my sandwiches.

Question   What was the strangest thing you've ever seen at the seaside?

Roger   Two elephants being chased off the beach.

Question   What were two elephants doing on the beach, and why were they being chased off?

Roger   Well, they'd come for a swim but they only had one pair of trunks between them.

Adi's favourite seaside joke

What's the difference between a fish and a piano?

You can't tuna fish!

How to stay safe at the seaside

 Don't go into the sea if a red flag is flying on the beach.

 Don't swallow sea water – it tastes disgusting.

 Never go swimming out of your depth

 Don't eat and drink before going swimming – it may give you cramps.

 Always use sunscreen and wear a sunhat – though your hat doesn't have to have the words 'Kiss me quick' written on it.

 Don't go out of sight of your family and friends, but do arrange a meeting place in case you get lost.

Don't fall asleep on your lilo – you might wake up in France.

 Watch out for strong currents and winds. They could carry you away from the beach.

 Dial 999 if you see anyone in trouble at sea.

Fantastic facts about the seashore

1 The coastline of Britain is 4000 kilometres long – so don't try to go round it in a pedalo.

2 Seaweeds are used to make toothpaste. Yuk!

3 Limpets begin life as boys and then become girls. Weird!

4 Seahorses aren't horses at all. They're small fish.

5 This isn't the only odd thing about seahorses. Male seahorses are the only male animals in the world to give birth.

Seashore lingo

Grockle A name for a visitor to the seaside – not a type of shellfish.

Sea squirt A little sea creature which fixes itself to a rock and then eats its own brain. It's nearly as dumb as Gummy.

Sea wrack A type of seaweed.

Shipwreck A sunken ship. Not to be confused with a nervous wreck – that's a sunken ship that lies on the bottom of the sea and shakes.

Tidal bore This is a wave as high as a wall – not a man who drones on and on and on about the sea.

Mystery Mob

Mystery Mob Set 1:

Mystery Mob and the Abominable Snowman
Mystery Mob and the Big Match
Mystery Mob and the Circus of Doom
Mystery Mob and the Creepy Castle
Mystery Mob and the Haunted Attic
Mystery Mob and the Hidden Treasure
Mystery Mob and the Magic Bottle
Mystery Mob and the Missing Millions
Mystery Mob and the Monster on the Moor
Mystery Mob and the Mummy's Curse
Mystery Mob and the Time Machine
Mystery Mob and the UFO

Mystery Mob Set 2:

Mystery Mob and the Ghost Town
Mystery Mob and the Bonfire Night Plot
Mystery Mob and the April Fools' Day Joker
Mystery Mob and the Great Pancake Day Race
Mystery Mob and the Scary Santa
Mystery Mob and the Conker Conspiracy
Mystery Mob and the Top Talent Contest
Mystery Mob and the Night in the Waxworks
Mystery Mob and the Runaway Train
Mystery Mob and the Wrong Robot
Mystery Mob and the Day of the Dinosaurs
Mystery Mob and the Man-eating Tiger

RISING ★ STARS